The Ready-Made Kids Quiz

Volume II

Compiled by Mark Lloyd

Published By
Pillar International Publishing Ltd
www.IndiePillar.com

© Mark Lloyd 2016
All Rights Reserved

Associate Editor: Jack Lloyd
Book and Cover Design: Lotte Bender
Cover Image: Lotte Bender

ISBN: 978-1-911303-06-0

Dedication

For Aideen, Fintan and Aisling

Introduction

As a child, I loved quizzes and puzzles. School quizzes, quiz books, TV quizzes, radio quizzes. I could not get enough of them.

I'm hoping here in this short book to ignite a love for quizzes and puzzles in the next generation.

My grandfather, Victor Lloyd, loved quizzes and crossword puzzles and published many fine quiz books in the original Pillar Publishing Dublin in the 1930s and 40s.

It is also to honour him that I create these books.

The questions vary in difficulty from easy to not so easy, but I have stayed away from questions that are overly difficult to allow for a greater overall feeling of inclusion, competition and entertainment.
Enjoy!

Mark.

Direct any feedback or corrections to:
info@indiepillar.com.

QUIZ 1: Round 1

1. What fruit would you dry to make a raisin?
2. How many horses are there in a game of water polo?
3. From what animal do we get ham?
4. In what French city would you find 'The Louvre'?
5. What is a Manx cat missing?
6. How many rings are on the Olympic flag?
7. What instrument does Lisa Simpson play?
8. What is the name given to the kitchen on a plane or boat?
9. Muse is an anagram for which flightless birds?
10. What is the name given to a 140 character update on twitter?

QUIZ 1: Round 2

1. What do maggots grow into?
2. *Coraline's* 'other mother' doesn't have eyes. What does she have instead?
3. What movie character says: "To infinity and beyond!"?
4. How many days in a leap year?
5. Who wrote 'The Grinch'?
6. From what English city do scousers hail?
7. With what sport do we associate Chris Boardman?
8. Traditionally, how many years are between each Olympic Games?
9. What is the name given to a female elephant?
10. What beast features on the Welsh flag?

QUIZ 1: Round 3

1. What does Hydroelectricity use to create power?
2. What does the first 'D' in DVD stand for?
3. What is added to an ice-cream cone to make it a 99?
4. What sweet is the nickname of Everton F.C.?
5. What metal alloy is used for a third place medal, traditionally?
6. What is the name of the imaginary line half-way between the North and South poles?
7. In text-speak, what does IMO stand for?
8. How many sides does an octagon have?
9. Who composed 'Twinkle, twinkle, little star'?
10. Which of these words is a *proper noun* - Robert, cheese or glamorous?

QUIZ 1: Round 4

1. What colour are the triple word score squares in Scrabble?
2. In the internet, what does the second 'W' in WWW stand for?
3. Which Italian city is famous for its leaning tower?
4. Which superhero's enemies include the Joker and The Riddler?
5. When a tennis player scores from a serve and the opponent fails to make contact with the ball, what is this called?
6. How many of Henry VIII's wives were beheaded?
7. What should a golfer shout to warn other players of an incoming ball?
8. What film character has been played by Roger Moore, Sean Connery and George Lazenby?
9. Who wrote the book 'Chitty Chitty Bang Bang'?
10. Penne and Linguine are types of what?

QUIZ 1: Round 5

1. With what sport would you normally associate Anna Kournikova?
2. In the *Tomb Raider* series, what was the name of the principal character?
3. Who hunted the Roadrunner in the cartoons?
4. What three-letter vessel is normally used to make a stir-fry?
5. What type of winged animal was the mythical Pegasus?
6. In the *Harry Potter* series, who was 'He who shall not be named'?
7. What is the name of the mayor of Springfield in *The Simpsons*?
8. In the game Connect 4, one set of counters is red but what colour are the others?
9. In what country is Snowdonia?
10. What nurse was known as 'The Lady with the Lamp'?

QUIZ 1: Round 6

1. From what country do we get Edam cheese?
2. Before the Euro, what was the currency in Spain?
3. In what country do the teams Empoli and Lazio play soccer?
4. What country would you most associate Mahatma Gandhi with?
5. Where is The Sea of Tranquillity?
6. The name of which martial art literally mean 'empty hand'?
7. The name of which pastime literally means 'empty orchestra'?
8. In what 1939 film did Dorothy have a dog called Toto?
9. What is the Roman numeral for one hundred?
10. From what country do we get the paper craft of origami?

QUIZ 1: Round 7

1. Is coffee made from beans, seeds or pulses?
2. What is the currency of Japan?
3. What would you do with a Gondola – Eat it, Drink it or Row it?
4. Traditionally, what leaves should you rub into a nettle sting?
5. Which U.S. city is known as 'The Windy City'?
6. Is a bat a mammal or a bird? Mammal
7. In what year was The Great Fire of London?
8. In what year was The Battle of Hastings? What nationality was Van Gogh?
9. On what major river is the city of Dublin, Ireland?

QUIZ 1: Round 8

1. What part of your body does an optometrist work on?
2. What does a philatelist collect?
3. Does a numismatist collect stones, coins or numbers?
4. Does a lepidopterist collect butterflies, mice or rubber bands?
5. If you were ambidextrous, which hand would you write with?
6. Triskaidekaphobia is the fear of what number?
7. Does a cartographer make menus, maps or mailboxes?
8. Does a bibliophile love books, bargains or baths?
9. What word is made up of the Greek for 'far away' and the Latin for 'sight'?
10. How many lines in a Limerick?

QUIZ 1: Round 9

1. What Jersey does the leader of the Tour de France wear?
2. In what sport do we have Twenty20 competitions?
3. What name is shared between a card game and a way to cross rivers?
4. What sea creature is used to make calamari?
5. In what mountain range is Mount Everest?
6. What name is shared by a book of maps and a North-African mountain range?
7. At Wimbledon, how many sets do you have to win to a men's match? Three
8. What is the name of the oven used by potters?
9. Dot dot dot, dash dash dash, dot dot dot – what is that in Morse code?
10. What is an *escargot* on your dinner plate?

QUIZ 1: Round 10

1. On what continent is Morocco?
2. What is the capital city of England?
3. In what country are the Pyramids of Giza?
4. Is Belize in Central America or North America?
5. What is the longest river in Africa?
6. On what island is the volcano Mount Etna?
7. To what country does the state of Chihuahua belong?
8. On what island is the parliament called the House of Keys?
9. This city is now called Beijing, what was it formerly known as?
10. Are penguins found in the Artic or the Antarctic?

QUIZ 2: Round 1

1. Is the scapula another name for A) The funny-bone B) The knee-cap C) The shoulder-blade?
2. Where in your body would you find the iris?
3. How many legs does an insect have?
4. What is the lightest known gas – Hydrogen, Helium or Air?
5. In Roman Numerals, what does 'x' stand for?
6. What does a cobbler make and repair?
7. How many pockets are there on a snooker table?
8. What is the name of the town where Fred Flintstone lives?
9. In what city was Batman based?
10. What is Superman's real name?

QUIZ 2: Round 2

1. What politician lives at No.10 Downing Street?
2. In golf, what name is given to a two under par score on a hole?
3. Tsar Nicholas II was once the ruler of which country?
4. What word beginning with 'a' connects something you wear when cleaning and a place for planes to park?
5. What birds could be found in a gaggle?
6. How many children did Queen Elizabeth I of England have?
7. From what South-American country does singer Shakira hail?
8. What meat does a Vegan eat?
9. What kind of dictionary do you use to find words with similar meanings?
10. What is the national language of Mexico?

QUIZ 2: Round 3

1. What was the name of the paper used by Egyptians to write on in ancient times?
2. In what sport would you do the butterfly or the breaststroke?
3. In the *Ben 10* cartoons, what is Ben's surname?
4. If I was in Paris eating a "baguette" what would I be eating?
5. How many points do you get for a try in Rugby Union?
6. What Ukrainian city gives its name to a chicken and garlic dish?
7. Who composed 'the Four Seasons'?
8. Who is credited with the invention of the telephone?
9. In what language does "noir" mean black?
10. In what country was soccer player Gareth Bale born?

QUIZ 2: Round 4

1. What comes after Alpha, Beta, Gamma?
2. In what country would you find the Nile Delta?
3. What would a Japanese person do with Nori – sail it, eat it, bury it for good luck?
4. For what country does Cesc Fabregas play soccer?
5. What is 'five' in French?
6. What is 'five' in Spanish?
7. What is 'five' in Italian?
8. What is the capital of Australia?
9. Polaris is another name for which star?
10. What are the three colours of the French flag?

QUIZ 2: Round 5

1. In what country would you find the city of Bangalore?
2. In what country would you find the city of Lahore?
3. Name a country beginning with the letter 'O'?
4. Name a country beginning with the letter 'Q'?
5. Name a country beginning with the letter 'Y'?
   Wow – they were hard!
6. What is the capital city of The Netherlands?
7. In what country would you find Washington D.C.?
8. In what country would you find The Grand Canyon?
9. In what country would you find Lough Neagh?
10. What country has a maple leaf on its flag?

QUIZ 2: Round 6

1. What is the biggest bone in your body?
2. Greenland is a territory of which European country?
3. What is the name of Horrid Henry's younger brother?
4. Sacramento is the capital of which U.S. State?
5. Which cartoon character says 'What's up Doc'?
6. What is the capital city of France?
7. Goldfinger was a baddie in which series of films?
8. What are Kalahari and Gobi – cheeses, instruments or deserts?
9. What are St. Agur, Red Leicester and Double Gloucester - cheeses, instruments or deserts?
10. What are Balalaika, Sitar and Theremin – cheeses, instruments or deserts?

QUIZ 2: Round 7

1. What would you do with a Fufu – wear it, sleep on it, or eat it?
2. What would you do with a Tutu – wear it, sleep on it, or eat it?
3. What would you do with a Muumuu – wear it, sleep on it, or eat it?
4. What planet is named after the Roman god of war?
5. What is the main ingredient of guacamole?
6. What might chase you through the streets of Pamplona in July every year? Bulls
7. Tallahassee is the capital of which U.S. State?
8. If you had 'neeps' with your haggis, what would you be eating?
9. In the play 'Hamlet', what kind of royalty is he?
10. What do you call a female Peacock?

QUIZ 2: Round 8

1. Where did NASA deploy the Lunar Rover – The Sun, The Moon, Mars?
2. What is the name of the muscle that pumps blood around your body?
3. How many animals of each kind did Moses take onto the Ark?
4. In Goldilocks, whose porridge was *just right*?
5. What did ancient Romans do in a vomitorium – read, get sick or wash?
6. What is the highest-ranking belt in Karate?
7. Honolulu is the capital of which U.S. State?
8. If you had 'tatties' with your haggis, what would you be eating?
9. What fruit is dried to make prunes?
10. What country has the Bundestag as its national parliament?

QUIZ 2: Round 9

1. What was the name of King Arthur's sword?
2. How many are in a quintet?
3. Beginning with 'O', what is the capital of Canada?
4. In the *Famous Five*, what was the name of the dog?
5. What flower is worn in England to remember those lost in the wars?
6. Great White, Blue and Killer are types of which marine animal?
7. What is the lowest-ranking belt in Karate?
8. Diana Prince is the name used by which superhero?
9. In which ice-based sport would you use a broom and a stone?
10. What is the name given to the water-filled trench around a castle?

QUIZ 2: Round 10

1. In Gaelic Football, how many points do you get for a goal?
2. What canal links the Atlantic and Pacific?
3. In what country was the Panama hat invented?
4. What are Trilbys, Deerstalkers and Stovepipes?
5. How many dimes in a dollar?
6. Is a cucumber a fruit or vegetable?
7. In your body, where would you find the cortex and the cerebellum?
8. In what sport can you be caught travelling and double-dribbling?
9. Who wrote the Alex Rider books?
10. With what sport would you associate Babe Ruth?

QUIZ 3: Round 1

1. Lisbon is the capital city of which European country?
2. Which superhero goes by the name of Bruce Banner?
3. In which sport might you see a googly?
4. What type of art would you associate with Banksy – Street Art, Sculpting or Landscapes?
5. How many cents in 10 Euro?
6. How many strings are on a classical guitar?
7. What was the name of the fox in *Dora the Explorer*?
8. In the NATO Phonetic Alphabet, what word is used to mean 'E'?
9. What name is given to a group of dolphins?
10. Where was the Samurai once a warrior – Egypt, England or Japan?

QUIZ 3: Round 2

1. Which comic book character wears a black and red striped jumper and has a dog called Gnasher?
2. Which Saint's day falls on February 14th?
3. If I am lactose intolerant do I have a problem digesting wheat, dairy or fruit?
4. Is the Lambada is a well-known cheese, car or dance?
5. In what country would you find New South Wales?
6. What is the name of Posh Spice's footballing husband? David Beckham
7. What would I use the Beaufort scale to measure?
8. In tennis, what name given to the stroke where the ball is returned before it has bounced?
9. What name is given to a group of whales?
10. What former nuclear-bomb testing site gives its name to a type of beachwear?

QUIZ 3: Round 3

1. What creatures did St. Patrick supposedly chase out of Ireland?
2. What 'D' is the only way a bishop can move in chess?
3. What 'D' is the street in the *Harry Potter* series where the wand shop is located?
4. In what country would you find British Colombia?
5. What mythical monster has one eye in the middle of its forehead?
6. What would I use the Celsius scale to measure?
7. What is the name of the breakfast food made from pigs' blood?
8. What is the name of the tunnel that joins England and France?
9. In what country is a motorway called an *Autoroute*?
10. What colour make the first move in chess?

QUIZ 3: Round 4

1. Who is the patron saint of Wales?
2. In Greek legend, what 'H' was left in the box that Pandora shut?
3. What is the lightest gas?
4. What 'P' was famously destroyed when Vesuvius erupted in AD 79?
5. What comical superhero's real name is Benny Krupp?
6. What is the name given to the Inuit house made of ice?
7. Where does a Mancunian live?
8. What is the current name of the city once known as Constantinople?
9. In what country is a motorway called an *Autostrada*?
10. What 'M' is used to classify animals that carry their young in their pouch?

QUIZ 3: Round 5

1. How many strings does a standard violin have?
2. What type of food are Madras, Thai Green and Balti?
3. What is the second-lightest gas? Helium
4. In the Wizard of Oz, what city was Dorothy's home?
5. Does a hydrophobic person fear electricity, eels or water?
6. What is the main ingredient of an omelette?
7. What force did Isaac Newton describe after an apple fell on his head?
8. In what sport would you find a driver, a wedge and a tee?
9. In what country is a motorway called an *Autobahn*?
10. How many years in a century?

QUIZ 3: Round 6

1. What in the body gives its name to the centre of a hurricane?
2. What type of food are Hawaiian, Four Seasons and Marguerita?
3. What name was given to the war boats of the Vikings?
4. What city's airport was named after John Lennon?
5. What is the traditional dessert served at Wimbledon?
6. What is wrapped around meat and sauce in an enchilada?
7. Which 1066 battle features on the Bayeux tapestry?
8. What industry uses ISBN numbers?
9. From which UK city do we get *Brummies*?
10. How many years in a millennium?

QUIZ 3: Round 7

1. Which of these can a vegan eat – Beef, Milk or Peanuts?
2. What colour is associated with jealousy?
3. The WHO is the World <blank> Organisation – fill in the blank!
4. What city was supposedly founded by Romulus and Remus?
5. Where is something from if it is occidental?
6. Which planet is known as The Red Planet?
7. What type of animal is a flying fox?
8. How many colours in the rainbow?
9. What is the name given to the official survey that counts a country's population?
10. Which U.S. city is nick-named 'The Big Apple'?

QUIZ 3: Round 8

1. What country gave The Statue of Liberty to America?
2. What colour do we normally associate with cowardice?
3. Where would you find a portcullis – a Fridge, a Castle or a Sink?
4. What is the closest planet to the Sun?
5. What is The Scouts' motto?
6. What profession once carried the nickname 'Bobbies'?
7. What music group featured Sting and Andy Summers?
8. What would you do in a sporting velodrome?
9. What are Bactrian and Dromedary types of?
10. When an airplane makes a sonic boom, what speed barrier is it said to have broken?

QUIZ 3: Round 9

1. True or False - Your retina is in your eye?
2. True or False - Vivaldi composed the Four Seasons?
3. True or False – The Great Barrier Reef is off the Canadian Coast?
4. True or False - A fly-half is a player in baseball?
5. True or False – Nelson Mandela was born in America?
6. True or False - Roquefort is a type of smelly cheese?
7. True or False – *The Canterbury Tales* were written by Chaucer?
8. True or False - The 'V' in DVD stands for 'versatile'?
9. True or False – The highest score in darts is achieved by hitting the bull?
10. True or False – Yuri Gagarin was the first man in space?

QUIZ 3: Round 10

1. According to the Bible, how many disciples did Jesus have?
2. As of 2016, how many times have Liverpool won the English Premier League?
3. How many minutes in a day?
4. How many days in a leap year?
5. How many players on one soccer team can play on the pitch at the same time?
6. How many dwarves lived with Snow White?
7. What number of people have walked on the moon?
8. How many years in a decade and a half?
9. How many pictures in a triptych?
10. How many Wonders of the Ancient World were there?

QUIZ 4: Round 1

1. What is the name given to a male duck?
2. Which admiral defeated the Spanish Armada in 1588?
3. Painted Lady, Comma and Red Admiral are types of what winged-insect?
4. In punctuation, what name is given to a comma with a dot above it?
5. What do you add to a colon to make a smiley face?
6. What 'p' is another name for brackets?
7. Billy-Ray Cyrus is the parent of which famous pop singer?
8. Which Mediterranean island-state has the capital Nicosia?
9. Is a Cypress a tree, a badger or a bottle-shape?
10. What can I get in a Nebuchadnezzar, a Magnum or a Jeroboam?

QUIZ 4: Round 2

1. What wooden animal did soldiers hide in at the battle of Troy?
2. Are anchovies fish, lettuce leaves or spices?
3. What name do we give to ancient embalmed Egyptian bodies?
4. What is the name given to the area that boxers fight in?
5. In snooker, what is a red ball worth?
6. What car company manufactured the Escort, the Sierra and the Granada?
7. How many goals in a hat-trick?
8. In what country would you find a mountain range called the Apennines?
9. Which Mediterranean island state has the capital Valetta?
10. What is passed between runners in a relay race?

QUIZ 4: Round 3

1. In what part of Achilles' body was he struck with the arrow that killed him?
2. Is calamari made from squid, lettuce leaves or beef?
3. Which famous Pharaoh's tomb was discovered in November 1922 by Howard Carter?
4. Is a crampon something used by boxers, climbers or welders?
5. In what part of the body would you find your calf muscles?
6. What is the singular of graffiti? Graffito
7. What 'A' is Britain's only poisonous snake?
8. Towards what city do Muslims face when they pray?
9. First launched in 1957, what was Sputnik?
10. What is true caviar made from?

QUIZ 4: Round 4

1. How many people walked on the moon on the first moon landing?
2. In what country would you find the Monza racetrack?
3. What 'H' is red and used to trick people in mystery novels?
4. Found on Salisbury plain in England, what 'S' is an ancient stone circle?
5. Which children's character asks – 'Can we fix it?
6. What is the plural of cactus?
7. With what sport would you normally associate Mark Spitz?
8. Which Englishman did Amundsen beat to the South Pole?
9. Which pungent foodstuff, beginning with 'G' comes in bulbs and cloves?
10. In what city would you find the Wailing Wall?

QUIZ 4: Round 5

1. What is the name given to iron pyrite, which looks very like gold but isn't?
2. What Arizona tourist attraction is 277 miles long and can be up to 18 miles wide?
3. The foundation for which badly-built Italian bell-tower was laid in 1173?
4. Which is the second planet from the Sun?
5. Traditionally, what is churned to make butter?
6. Which king was briefly married to Anne Boleyn?
7. What is the only planet in our solar system not named after a god?
8. From which precious stone do we get a common nickname for Ireland?
9. How many seats are there in a Formula 1 racing car?
10. What are tarragon and sage?

QUIZ 4: Round 6

1. Which of these is an extinct bird – Emu, Dodo or Swan?
2. In what language does *sayonara* mean goodbye?
3. In what language does *au revoir* mean goodbye?
4. In what film series did Marty McFly travel in time?
5. Who painted the ceiling of the Sistine Chapel?
6. What is the name given to the pieces of wood that sit atop the stumps in cricket?
7. What is the fastest bird on land?
8. What country governs the islands of Crete and Kos?
9. What country governs the island of Corsica?
10. What country governs the island of Sicily?

QUIZ 4: Round 7

1. What is the nickname of West Ham United Football Club?
2. What colour is Marge Simpson's hair?
3. In the film *Home Alone*, what is the name of the boy who gets left behind?
4. On a standard computer keyboard, what letter comes after 'T'?
5. What volcano erupted in AD79, destroying Pompeii?
6. Is the English Grand National horse race run at Ascot, Uttoxeter or Aintree?
7. What sea-going 'H' was invented by Christopher Cockerell?
8. What did Mary Poppins use to help her fly?
9. What do we call a female fox?
10. Which country fought The Falklands War against Britain?

QUIZ 4: Round 8

1. What is Port Salut – A cheese, a wine, a fish?
2. Did sliced bread first appear in the 1930s, 1940s or 1950s?
3. What miracle did Jesus perform at the wedding feast of Cana?
4. What are 'Ben and Jerry' famous for?
5. What name is given to the Swiss dish where food is dipped into melted cheese using skewers?
6. What nuts are used to make Marzipan – Almonds, walnuts or cashews?
7. From the milk of which animal is real mozzarella made?
8. Button, oyster and shitake are varieties of what?
9. Traditionally, for how many minutes is steak tartare cooked?
10. What are habanero and scotch bonnet varieties of?

QUIZ 4: Round 9

1. What superhero's real name is Clark Kent?
2. From what fruit is champagne made?
3. What is the largest country in South America?
4. What breakfast cereal was said to go 'Snap, Crackle and Pop'?
5. In New York's JFK airport, what does the 'K' stand for?
6. Is there a net in the game of squash?
7. From what country did the USA buy Alaska?
8. From what country did the USA buy Louisiana?
9. What sport follows the Queensbury Rules – Boxing, weightlifting or fishing?
10. With which band was Freddie Mercury the lead singer – Bread, Soap or Queen?

QUIZ 4: Round 10

1. Dot-Matrix, Laser and Inkjet are types of what technological device?
2. What type of software are Chrome, Explorer and Safari?
3. What does the 'V in 'VDU' stand for?
4. What country has the internet domain '.ru'?
5. What would you use Hotmail, Gmail or Outlook to check?
6. What company bought Instagram in 2012?
7. What is the total number of characters that are allowed in a tweet on Twitter?
8. What company was founded by, amongst others, Mark Zuckerberg in 2004?
9. What did the island of Tuvalu do with their '.tv' internet domain in 1998?
10. What are C++, Visual Basic and FORTRAN?

QUIZ 5: Round 1

1. Which equestrian sport might feature a pirouette or a half-pass?
2. Which Olympic competition features ten separate sub-competitions including 100 Metres and Long Jump?
3. Which Brazilian city won the right to host the 2016 Olympics?
4. What is the name of the Olympics' governing body?
5. What is the highest mountain in Greece?
6. In what country were the 1896 Olympic Games held?
7. True or False – Ireland's first Olympic medal was in painting?
8. Why were the 1916 Olympics cancelled?
9. What name is given to those who have competed in the Olympics?
10. Which type of Olympics was first held in 1924?

QUIZ 5: Round 2

1. What type of craft exploded in May 1937 to cause the Hindenburg disaster?
2. What famous ship sank on April 15th 1912?
3. Why did the RMS Lusitania sink on the 7th of May 1915?
4. What is the name given to a giant wave caused by an earthquake at sea?
5. What is the name given to a war where all the participants are from the same country?
6. Which civil war featured the Roundheads and the Cavaliers?
7. What did the 'Enola Gay' drop first in World War II?
8. What was the nickname of World War II general Erwin Rommel?
9. Which U.S. TV series centered on the passengers of Oceanic flight 815?
10. Which war ended with the Treaty of Versailles in 1919?

QUIZ 5: Round 3

1. What triangle is the area in the Atlantic where planes and boats have mysteriously disappeared?
2. What *circus* in London is home to a statue of Eros?
3. What square in Moscow is home to the resting place of Lenin?
4. What cube was the UK's best-selling Christmas gift in 1980?
5. What shape describes the HQ of the US Department of Defense?
6. What circle do illusionists belong to?
7. How many sides does a quadrilateral have?
8. What imaginary line is half-way between the North and South Poles?
9. What shape's name comes from the Greek 'kulindros', meaning roller?
10. Over what letters of the alphabet would you find a tittle?

QUIZ 5: Round 4

1. What type of creatures featured in the Jurassic Park movies?
2. What type of transport was Amelia Earhart associated with?
3. In the Highland Games, what would I do with a caber?
4. What is the name of the lead-singer with U2?
5. What were the Amstrad CPC464, the ZX Spectrum and the Commodore 64?
6. Traditionally, what colour is a baseball?
7. What vegetable give Popeye his strength?
8. What creature has varieties such as Black Widow and Tarantula?
9. What is the national language of Brazil?
10. What do Americans celebrate on the 4th of July?

QUIZ 5: Round 5

1. In the Star Wars movies, who did Anakin Skywalker become?
2. In 2000, what country was added to rugby's Five Nations – Italy, Spain or Germany?
3. In what UK city is 'EastEnders' set?
4. With what sport do we normally associate Chris Evert-Lloyd?
5. In what country do we find communal farms called *Kibbutz*?
6. What is the profession of Mario of Super Mario Brothers fame?
7. What type of flag traditionally greets the winner of a motor race?
8. What English Christian name corresponds to the following names – Ivan, Sean, Juan and Giovanni?
9. What number is directly below '6' on most numeric keypads?
10. What do solar panels harness to make electricity?

QUIZ 5: Round 6

1. Which polar inhabitant is the fastest swimming bird?
2. What beer does Homer Simpson normally drink?
3. What is the principal item in a Panda's diet?
4. Shrove Tuesday is another name for what culinary day?
5. How many stripes are on the U.S. flag?
6. What type of sea creature is a Portuguese Man of War?
7. 'Polo' aftershave is made by which popular fashion brand?
8. What animal is known as "Man's best friend"?
9. What number is directly below '7' on most numeric keypads?
10. What jubilee was celebrated when Queen Elizabeth the second was 50 years on the throne?

QUIZ 5: Round 7

1. From what country do we get the soaps 'Neighbours' and 'Home and Away'?
2. On what river does the Oxford and Cambridge boat race take place?
3. On what would you find a porthole and a deck?
4. In snooker, in a 147 break, what colour is the last ball to be potted?
5. What does the 'F' in UFO stand for?
6. The Statue of Liberty holds a book in one hand and what item in the other?
7. Over what country did the Ming Dynasty rule?
8. What company makes the iPhone?
9. What highwayman had a horse called Black Bess?
10. After which painter is Rome's Fiumicino airport named?

QUIZ 5: Round 8

1. What is another name for a 'sleeping policeman', used to slow down cars on roads?
2. In televisions, what does the 'L' in LCD stand for?
3. Which Asian country used to be called Cathay?
4. Which saint is associated with the town of Lourdes, France?
5. If something is described as pneumatic, is it powered by air, water or sunlight?
6. In text-speak, what does LOL stand for?
7. What general's 'Last Stand' was at the Battle of Little Bighorn?
8. What is the name of the now disused prison on an island in San Francisco Bay?
9. In boxing, if you 'throw in the towel', what does that mean?
10. In what part of the house would you most likely find a wok or a bain marie?

QUIZ 5: Round 9

1. What type of drink might a *merlot* or a *rioja* be?
2. Which is larger, Mars or Earth?
3. What swordsman was famous for leaving a 'Z' behind him?
4. In the legends of King Arthur, which 'M' was a wizard?
5. What 'G' is a British overseas territory that borders Spain?
6. Tug-of-War used to be an Olympic event, True or False?
7. Who was the other half of Stan Laurel's comedy duo?
8. What is *Manchego* – a cheese, a board-game or a car manufacturer?
9. In what country would you find Mount Rushmore?
10. What group of people believed in Valhalla and Asgard?

QUIZ 5: Round 10

1. What, according to the saying, do birds of a feather do?
2. In semaphore, what 'f' is used to communicate?
3. In what Herman Melville book does Captain Ahab hunt a whale?
4. In *Harry Potter*, what must be given to a house elf to free it?
5. What country's capital is Prague?
6. Which Shakespeare play is known as 'the Scottish Play' because it is unlucky for actors to use its real name?
7. What 'H' is measured using the Carvill scale?
8. With what island do we associate the Manx cat?
9. In Greek mythology, who turned all he touched to gold?
10. What 'R' is a sport invented by William Webb-Ellis?

Tie Breakers

20 Tie-Breakers

1. In Lear's poem, who travelled in a 'beautiful pea-green boat'?
2. In the Hunger Games films, who plays Katniss Everdeen?
3. What type of animals are Fiver, Hazel and Bigwig from *Watership Down*?
4. In what country is the Yuan the currency?
5. In the children's series, what is the name of the *Big Red Dog*?
6. How many degrees do you turn if you make a full circle?
7. The word 'Plumber' comes from the Latin word for which metal?
8. In cricket, how many runs do you need for a double-century?
9. On what continent would you find Zaire?
10. What is the smallest of the world's oceans?
11. Alphabetically, what day of the week comes first?
12. Which children's character is a bear with two birthdays that comes from Peru?
13. In what country would you find the Taj Mahal?
14. What 'M' is the name given to a type of animal that carries its babies in a pouch?
15. Complete the saying – "A stitch in time, saves ____"?

16. What was Don Quixote known for tilting at?
17. What is the capital of Scotland?
18. In *Charlie and the Chocolate Factory*, what is Charlie's surname?
19. What two countries are connected by The Channel Tunnel?
20. How many members were left in *One Direction* after Zayn left?

The Answers Section

QUIZ 1: Round 1

1. What fruit would you dry to make a raisin? Grape
2. How many horses are there in a game of water polo? None
3. From what animal do we get ham? Pig
4. In what French city would you find 'The Louvre'? Paris
5. What is a Manx cat missing? A tail
6. How many rings are on the Olympic flag? 5
7. What instrument does Lisa Simpson play? Saxophone
8. What is the name given to the kitchen on a plane or boat? Galley
9. Muse is an anagram for which flightless birds? Emus
10. What is the name given to a 140 character update on twitter? A tweet

QUIZ 1: Round 2

1. What do maggots grow into? Flies (Ugh!)
2. *Coraline's* 'other mother' doesn't have eyes. What does she have instead? Buttons
3. What movie character says: "To infinity and beyond!"? Buzz Lightyear
4. How many days in a leap year? 366
5. Who wrote 'The Grinch'? Dr. Seuss
6. From what English city do scousers hail? Liverpool
7. With what sport do we associate Chris Boardman? Cycling
8. Traditionally, how many years are between each Olympic Games? 4
9. What is the name given to a female elephant? Cow
10. What beast features on the Welsh flag? Dragon

QUIZ 1: Round 3

1. What does Hydroelectricity use to create power? Water
2. What does the first 'D' in DVD stand for? Digital
3. What is added to an ice-cream cone to make it a 99? Flake
4. What sweet is the nickname of Everton F.C.? Toffees
5. What metal alloy is used for a third place medal, traditionally? Bronze
6. What is the name of the imaginary line half-way between the North and South poles? Equator
7. In text-speak, what does IMO stand for? In my opinion
8. How many sides does an octagon have? 8
9. Who composed 'Twinkle, twinkle, little star'? Mozart
10. Which of these words is a *proper noun* - Robert, cheese or glamorous? Robert

QUIZ 1: Round 4

1. What colour are the triple word score squares in Scrabble? Red
2. In the internet, what does the second 'W' in WWW stand for? Wide
3. Which Italian city is famous for its leaning tower? Pisa
4. Which superhero's enemies include the Joker and The Riddler? Batman
5. When a tennis player scores from a serve and the opponent fails to make contact with the ball, what is this called? An ace
6. How many of Henry VIII's wives were beheaded? Two
7. What should a golfer shout to warn other players of an incoming ball? Fore
8. What film character has been played by Roger Moore, Sean Connery and George Lazenby? James Bond
9. Who wrote the book 'Chitty Chitty Bang Bang'? Ian Fleming
10. Penne and Linguine are types of what? Pasta

QUIZ 1: Round 5

1. With what sport would you normally associate Anna Kournikova? Tennis
2. In the *Tomb Raider* series, what was the name of the principal character? Lara Croft
3. Who hunted the Roadrunner in the cartoons? Wile E. Coyote
4. What three-letter vessel is normally used to make a stir-fry? Wok
5. What type of winged animal was the mythical Pegasus? A horse
6. In the *Harry Potter* series, who was 'He who shall not be named'? Lord Voldemort
7. What is the name of the mayor of Springfield in *The Simpsons*? Mayor Quimby
8. In the game Connect 4, one set of counters is red but what colour are the others? Yellow
9. In what country is Snowdonia? Wales
10. What nurse was known as 'The Lady with the Lamp'? Florence Nightingale

QUIZ 1: Round 6

1. From what country do we get Edam cheese?
   The Netherlands
2. Before the Euro, what was the currency in
   Spain? Peseta
3. In what country do the teams Empoli and
   Lazio play soccer? Italy
4. What country would you most associate
   Mahatma Gandhi with? India
5. Where is The Sea of Tranquillity? The Moon
6. The name of which martial art literally mean
   'empty hand'? karate
7. The name of which pastime literally means
   'empty orchestra'? karaoke
8. In what 1939 film did Dorothy have a dog
   called Toto? The Wizard of Oz
9. What is the Roman numeral for one hundred?
   C
10. From what country do we get the paper craft
    of origami? Japan

QUIZ 1: Round 7

1. Is coffee made from beans, seeds or pulses? Beans
2. What is the currency of Japan? Yen
3. What would you do with a Gondola – Eat it, Drink it or Row it? Row it
4. Traditionally, what leaves should you rub into a nettle sting? Dock
5. Which U.S. city is known as 'The Windy City'? Chicago
6. Is a bat a mammal or a bird? Mammal
7. In what year was The Great Fire of London? 1666
8. In what year was The Battle of Hastings? 1066
9. What nationality was Van Gogh? Dutch
10. On what major river is the city of Dublin, Ireland? Liffey

QUIZ 1: Round 8

1. What part of your body does an optometrist work on? Eyes
2. What does a philatelist collect? Stamps
3. Does a numismatist collect stones, coins or numbers? Coins
4. Does a lepidopterist collect butterflies, mice or rubber bands? Butterflies
5. If you were ambidextrous, which hand would you write with? Either hand
6. Triskaidekaphobia is the fear of what number? 13
7. Does a cartographer make menus, maps or mailboxes? Maps
8. Does a bibliophile love books, bargains or baths? Books
9. What word is made up of the Greek for 'far away' and the Latin for 'sight'? [Hint: It's in your house] Television
10. How many lines in a Limerick? 5

QUIZ 1: Round 9

1. What Jersey does the leader of the Tour de France wear? Yellow
2. In what sport do we have Twenty20 competitions? Cricket
3. What name is shared between a card game and a way to cross rivers? Bridge or pontoon
4. What sea creature is used to make calamari? Squid
5. In what mountain range is Mount Everest? The Himalayas
6. What name is shared by a book of maps and a North-African mountain range? Atlas
7. At Wimbledon, how many sets do you have to win to a men's match? Three
8. What is the name of the oven used by potters? Kiln
9. Dot dot dot, dash dash dash, dot dot dot – what is that in Morse code? S.O.S
10. What is an *escargot* on your dinner plate? Snail

QUIZ 1: Round 10

1. On what continent is Morocco? Africa
2. What is the capital city of England? London
3. In what country are the Pyramids of Giza? Egypt
4. Is Belize in Central America or North America? Central America
5. What is the longest river in Africa? The Nile
6. On what island is the volcano Mount Etna? Sicily
7. To what country does the state of Chihuahua belong? Mexico
8. On what island is the parliament called the House of Keys? The Isle of Man
9. This city is now called Beijing, what was it formerly known as? Peking
10. Are penguins found in the Artic or the Antarctic? Antarctic

QUIZ 2: Round 1

1. Is the scapula another name for A) The funny-bone B) The knee-cap C) The shoulder-blade? C) Shoulder-blade
2. Where in your body would you find the iris? Eye
3. How many legs does an insect have? 6
4. What is the lightest known gas – Hydrogen, Helium or Air? Hydrogen
5. In Roman Numerals, what does 'x' stand for? Ten
6. What does a cobbler make and repair? Shoes
7. How many pockets are there on a snooker table? 6
8. What is the name of the town where Fred Flintstone lives? Bedrock
9. In what city was Batman based? Gotham
10. What is Superman's real name? Clark Kent

QUIZ 2: Round 2

1. What politician lives at No.10 Downing Street? The British Prime Minister
2. In golf, what name is given to a two under par score on a hole? Eagle
3. Tsar Nicholas II was once the ruler of which country? Russia
4. What word beginning with 'a' connects something you wear when cleaning and a place for planes to park? Apron
5. What birds could be found in a gaggle? Geese
6. How many children did Queen Elizabeth I of England have? None
7. From what South-American country does singer Shakira hail? Colombia
8. What meat does a Vegan eat? None
9. What kind of dictionary do you use to find words with similar meanings? Thesaurus
10. What is the national language of Mexico? Spanish

QUIZ 2: Round 3

1. What was the name of the paper used by Egyptians to write on in ancient times? [Hint: begins with 'p'] Papyrus
2. In what sport would you do the butterfly or the breaststroke? Swimming
3. In the *Ben 10* cartoons, what is Ben's surname? Tennyson
4. If I was in Paris eating a "baguette" what would I be eating? Bread
5. How many points do you get for a try in Rugby Union? Five
6. What Ukrainian city gives its name to a chicken and garlic dish? Kiev
7. Who composed 'the Four Seasons'? Vivaldi
8. Who is credited with the invention of the telephone? Alexander Graham Bell
9. In what language does "noir" mean black? French
10. In what country was soccer player Gareth Bale born? Wales

QUIZ 2: Round 4

1. What comes after Alpha, Beta, Gamma? Delta
2. In what country would you find the Nile Delta? Egypt
3. What would a Japanese person do with Nori – sail it, eat it, bury it for good luck? Eat it - It's the seaweed roll used for Sushi
4. For what country does Cesc Fabregas play soccer? Spain
5. What is 'five' in French? Cinq (SANK)
6. What is 'five' in Spanish? Cinco (SINK-O)
7. What is 'five' in Italian? Cinque (CHIN-KWE)
8. What is the capital of Australia? Canberra
9. Polaris is another name for which star? The North Star
10. What are the three colours of the French flag? Red, white and blue

QUIZ 2: Round 5

1. In what country would you find the city of Bangalore? India
2. In what country would you find the city of Lahore? Pakistan
3. Name a country beginning with the letter 'O'? Oman
4. Name a country beginning with the letter 'Q'? Qatar
5. Name a country beginning with the letter 'Y'? Yemen
6. What is the capital city of The Netherlands? Amsterdam
7. In what country would you find Washington D.C.? USA
8. In what country would you find The Grand Canyon? USA
9. In what country would you find Lough Neagh? Northern Ireland
10. What country has a maple leaf on its flag? Canada

QUIZ 2: Round 6

1. What is the biggest bone in your body? Thigh bone or Femur
2. Greenland is a territory of which European country? Denmark
3. What is the name of Horrid Henry's younger brother? Perfect Peter
4. Sacramento is the capital of which U.S. State? California
5. Which cartoon character says 'What's up Doc'? Bugs Bunny
6. What is the capital city of France? Paris
7. Goldfinger was a baddie in which series of films? James Bond
8. What are Kalahari and Gobi – cheeses, instruments or deserts? Deserts
9. What are St. Agur, Red Leicester and Double Gloucester - cheeses, instruments or deserts? Cheeses
10. What are Balalaika, Sitar and Theremin – cheeses, instruments or deserts? Instruments

QUIZ 2: Round 7

1. What would you do with a Fufu – wear it, sleep on it, or eat it? Eat it – it's an African food
2. What would you do with a Tutu – wear it, sleep on it, or eat it? Wear it – it's a ballet dress
3. What would you do with a Muumuu – wear it, sleep on it, or eat it? Wear it – it's an Hawaiian dress
4. What planet is named after the Roman god of war? Mars
5. What is the main ingredient of guacamole? Avocado
6. What might chase you through the streets of Pamplona in July every year? Bulls
7. Tallahassee is the capital of which U.S. State? Florida
8. If you had 'neeps' with your haggis, what would you be eating? Turnips or swedes
9. In the play 'Hamlet', what kind of royalty is he? Prince (of Denmark to be precise)
10. What do you call a female Peacock? Peahen

QUIZ 2: Round 8

1. Where did NASA deploy the Lunar Rover – The Sun, The Moon, Mars? The Moon
2. What is the name of the muscle that pumps blood around your body? The heart
3. How many animals of each kind did Moses take onto the Ark? None – it was Noah
4. In Goldilocks, whose porridge was *just right*? Baby Bear's
5. What did ancient Romans do in a vomitorium – read, get sick or wash? Get sick (ugh)
6. What is the highest-ranking belt in Karate? Black belt
7. Honolulu is the capital of which U.S. State? Hawaii
8. If you had 'tatties' with your haggis, what would you be eating? Potatoes
9. What fruit is dried to make prunes? Plums
10. What country has the Bundestag as its national parliament? Germany

QUIZ 2: Round 9

1. What was the name of King Arthur's sword? Excalibur
2. How many are in a quintet? Five
3. Beginning with 'O', what is the capital of Canada? Ottawa
4. In the *Famous Five*, what was the name of the dog? Timmy
5. What flower is worn in England to remember those lost in the wars? Poppy
6. Great White, Blue and Killer are types of which marine animal? Whale
7. What is the lowest-ranking belt in Karate? White belt
8. Diana Prince is the name used by which superhero? Wonder Woman
9. In which ice-based sport would you use a broom and a stone? Curling
10. What is the name given to the water-filled trench around a castle? Moat

QUIZ 2: Round 10

1. In Gaelic Football, how many points do you get for a goal? Three
2. What canal links the Atlantic and Pacific? Panama
3. In what country was the Panama hat invented? Ecuador
4. What are Trilbys, Deerstalkers and Stovepipes? Hats
5. How many dimes in a dollar? 10
6. Is a cucumber a fruit or vegetable? Fruit
7. In your body, where would you find the cortex and the cerebellum? Your brain
8. In what sport can you be caught travelling and double-dribbling? Basketball
9. Who wrote the Alex Rider books? Anthony Horowitz
10. With what sport would you associate Babe Ruth? Baseball

QUIZ 3: Round 1

1. Lisbon is the capital city of which European country? Portugal
2. Which superhero goes by the name of Bruce Banner? The Hulk
3. In which sport might you see a googly? Cricket
4. What type of art would you associate with Banksy – Street Art, Sculpting or Landscapes? Street Art
5. How many cents in 10 Euro? 1000
6. How many strings are on a classical guitar? Six
7. What was the name of the fox in *Dora the Explorer*? Swiper
8. In the NATO Phonetic Alphabet, what word is used to mean 'E'? Echo
9. What name is given to a group of dolphins? Pod
10. Where was the Samurai once a warrior – Egypt, England or Japan? Japan

QUIZ 3: Round 2

1. Which comic book character wears a black and red striped jumper and has a dog called Gnasher? Dennis The Menace
2. Which Saint's day falls on February 14th? St. Valentine
3. If I am lactose intolerant do I have a problem digesting wheat, dairy or fruit? Dairy
4. Is the Lambada is a well-known cheese, car or dance? Dance
5. In what country would you find New South Wales? Australia
6. What is the name of Posh Spice's footballing husband? David Beckham
7. What would I use the Beaufort scale to measure? Wind
8. In tennis, what name given to the stroke where the ball is returned before it has bounced? Volley
9. What name is given to a group of whales? Pod
10. What former nuclear-bomb testing site gives its name to a type of beachwear? Bikini

QUIZ 3: Round 3

1. What creatures did St. Patrick supposedly chase out of Ireland? Snakes
2. What 'D' is the only way a bishop can move in chess? Diagonally
3. What 'D' is the street in the *Harry Potter* series where the wand shop is located? Diagon Alley
4. In what country would you find British Colombia? Canada
5. What mythical monster has one eye in the middle of its forehead? Cyclops
6. What would I use the Celsius scale to measure? Temperature
7. What is the name of the breakfast food made from pigs' blood? Black Pudding
8. What is the name of the tunnel that joins England and France? Channel Tunnel
9. In what country is a motorway called an *Autoroute*? France
10. What colour make the first move in chess? White

QUIZ 3: Round 4

1. Who is the patron saint of Wales? David
2. In Greek legend, what 'H' was left in the box that Pandora shut? Hope
3. What is the lightest gas? Hydrogen
4. What 'P' was famously destroyed when Vesuvius erupted in AD 79? Pompeii
5. What comical superhero's real name is Benny Krupp? Captain Underpants
6. What is the name given to the Inuit house made of ice? Igloo
7. Where does a Mancunian live? Manchester
8. What is the current name of the city once known as Constantinople? Istanbul
9. In what country is a motorway called an *Autostrada*? Italy
10. What 'M' is used to classify animals that carry their young in their pouch? Marsupial

QUIZ 3: Round 5

1. How many strings does a standard violin have? Four
2. What type of food are Madras, Thai Green and Balti? Curries
3. What is the second-lightest gas? Helium
4. In the Wizard of Oz, what city was Dorothy's home? Kansas
5. Does a hydrophobic person fear electricity, eels or water? Water
6. What is the main ingredient of an omelette? Egg
7. What force did Isaac Newton describe after an apple fell on his head? Gravity
8. In what sport would you find a driver, a wedge and a tee? Golf
9. In what country is a motorway called an *Autobahn*? Germany
10. How many years in a century? 100

QUIZ 3: Round 6

1. What in the body gives its name to the centre of a hurricane? The eye
2. What type of food are Hawaiian, Four Seasons and Marguerita? Pizzas
3. What name was given to the war boats of the Vikings? Longships
4. What city's airport was named after John Lennon? Liverpool
5. What is the traditional dessert served at Wimbledon? Strawberries and Cream
6. What is wrapped around meat and sauce in an enchilada? A tortilla
7. Which 1066 battle features on the Bayeux tapestry? The Battle of Hastings
8. What industry uses ISBN numbers? Publishing
9. From which UK city do we get *Brummies*? Birmingham
10. How many years in a millennium? 1000

QUIZ 3: Round 7

1. Which of these can a vegan eat – Beef, Milk or Peanuts? Peanuts
2. What colour is associated with jealousy? Green (with envy!)
3. The WHO is the World <blank> Organisation – fill in the blank! Health
4. What city was supposedly founded by Romulus and Remus? Rome
5. Where is something from if it is occidental? The West
6. Which planet is known as The Red Planet? Mars
7. What type of animal is a flying fox? A bat
8. How many colours in the rainbow? Seven
9. What is the name given to the official survey that counts a country's population? Census
10. Which U.S. city is nick-named 'The Big Apple'? New York

QUIZ 3: Round 8

1. What country gave The Statue of Liberty to America? France
2. What colour do we normally associate with cowardice? Yellow
3. Where would you find a portcullis – a Fridge, a Castle or a Sink? Castle
4. What is the closest planet to the Sun? Mercury
5. What is The Scouts' motto? 'Be Prepared'
6. What profession once carried the nickname 'Bobbies'? The Police
7. What music group featured Sting and Andy Summers? The Police
8. What would you do in a sporting velodrome? Cycle
9. What are Bactrian and Dromedary types of? Camels
10. When an airplane makes a sonic boom, what speed barrier is it said to have broken? The sound barrier or the speed of sound

QUIZ 3: Round 9

1. True or False - Your retina is in your eye? True
2. True or False - Vivaldi composed the Four Seasons? True
3. True or False – The Great Barrier Reef is off the Canadian Coast? False
4. True or False - A fly-half is a player in baseball? False
5. True or False – Nelson Mandela was born in America? False
6. True or False - Roquefort is a type of smelly cheese? True
7. True or False – *The Canterbury Tales* were written by Chaucer? True
8. True or False - The 'V' in DVD stands for 'versatile'? True
9. True or False – The highest score in darts is achieved by hitting the bull? False
10. True or False – Yuri Gagarin was the first man in space? True

QUIZ 3: Round 10

1. According to the Bible, how many disciples did Jesus have? 12
2. As of 2016, how many times have Liverpool won the English Premier League? Zero times
3. How many minutes in a day? 1440
4. How many days in a leap year? 366
5. How many players on one soccer team can play on the pitch at the same time? 11
6. How many dwarves lived with Snow White? 7
7. What number of people have walked on the moon? 12
8. How many years in a decade and a half? 15
9. How many pictures in a triptych? 3
10. How many Wonders of the Ancient World were there? 7

QUIZ 4: Round 1

1. What is the name given to a male duck? Drake
2. Which admiral defeated the Spanish Armada in 1588? Sir Francis Drake
3. Painted Lady, Comma and Red Admiral are types of what winged-insect? Butterflies
4. In punctuation, what name is given to a comma with a dot above it? Semi-colon
5. What do you add to a colon to make a smiley face? ')' Closed bracket
6. What 'p' is another name for brackets? Parentheses
7. Billy-Ray Cyrus is the parent of which famous pop singer? Miley Cyrus
8. Which Mediterranean island-state has the capital Nicosia? Cyprus
9. Is a Cypress a tree, a badger or a bottle-shape? Tree
10. What can I get in a Nebuchadnezzar, a Magnum or a Jeroboam? Wine or champagne – they are bottle sizes!

QUIZ 4: Round 2

1. What wooden animal did soldiers hide in at the battle of Troy? A horse
2. Are anchovies fish, lettuce leaves or spices? Fish
3. What name do we give to ancient embalmed Egyptian bodies? Mummies
4. What is the name given to the area that boxers fight in? The Ring
5. In snooker, what is a red ball worth? One point
6. What car company manufactured the Escort, the Sierra and the Granada? Ford
7. How many goals in a hat-trick? Three
8. In what country would you find a mountain range called the Apennines? Italy
9. Which Mediterranean island state has the capital Valetta? Malta
10. What is passed between runners in a relay race? The baton

QUIZ 4: Round 3

1. In what part of Achilles' body was he struck with the arrow that killed him? His heel
2. Is calamari made from squid, lettuce leaves or beef? Squid
3. Which famous Pharaoh's tomb was discovered in November 1922 by Howard Carter? Tutankhamun or King Tut
4. Is a crampon something used by boxers, climbers or welders? Climbers
5. In what part of the body would you find your calf muscles? Legs
6. What is the singular of graffiti? Graffito
7. What 'A' is Britain's only poisonous snake? An adder
8. Towards what city do Muslims face when they pray? Mecca
9. First launched in 1957, what was Sputnik? A satellite
10. What is true caviar made from? Fish eggs or roe

QUIZ 4: Round 4

1. How many people walked on the moon on the first moon landing? Two – Armstrong and Aldrin
2. In what country would you find the Monza racetrack? Italy
3. What 'H' is red and used to trick people in mystery novels? Herring
4. Found on Salisbury plain in England, what 'S' is an ancient stone circle? Stonehenge
5. Which children's character asks – 'Can we fix it?' Bob The Builder
6. What is the plural of cactus? Cacti
7. With what sport would you normally associate Mark Spitz? Swimming
8. Which Englishman did Amundsen beat to the South Pole? Robert Falcon Scott
9. Which pungent foodstuff, beginning with 'G' comes in bulbs and cloves? Garlic
10. In what city would you find the Wailing Wall? Jerusalem

QUIZ 4: Round 5

1. What is the name given to iron pyrite, which looks very like gold but isn't? Fool's gold
2. What Arizona tourist attraction is 277 miles long and can be up to 18 miles wide? The Grand Canyon
3. The foundation for which badly-built Italian bell-tower was laid in 1173? Leaning Tower of Pisa
4. Which is the second planet from the Sun? Venus
5. Traditionally, what is churned to make butter? Milk
6. Which king was briefly married to Anne Boleyn? Henry VIII
7. What is the only planet in our solar system not named after a god? Earth
8. From which precious stone do we get a common nickname for Ireland? The EMERALD Isle
9. How many seats are there in a Formula 1 racing car? One
10. What are tarragon and sage? Herbs

QUIZ 4: Round 6

1. Which of these is an extinct bird – Emu, Dodo or Swan? Dodo
2. In what language does *sayonara* mean goodbye? Japanese
3. In what language does *au revoir* mean goodbye? French
4. In what film series did Marty McFly travel in time? Back to the Future
5. Who painted the ceiling of the Sistine Chapel? Michelangelo
6. What is the name given to the pieces of wood that sit atop the stumps in cricket? Bails
7. What is the fastest bird on land? Ostrich
8. What country governs the islands of Crete and Kos? Greece
9. What country governs the island of Corsica? France
10. What country governs the island of Sicily? Italy

QUIZ 4: Round 7

1. What is the nickname of West Ham United Football Club? The Hammers
2. What colour is Marge Simpson's hair? Blue
3. In the film *Home Alone*, what is the name of the boy who gets left behind? Kevin
4. On a standard computer keyboard, what letter comes after 'T'? Y
5. What volcano erupted in AD79, destroying Pompeii? Vesuvius
6. Is the English Grand National horse race run at Ascot, Uttoxeter or Aintree? Aintree
7. What sea-going 'H' was invented by Christopher Cockerell? Hovercraft
8. What did Mary Poppins use to help her fly? Umbrella
9. What do we call a female fox? A Vixen
10. Which country fought The Falklands War against Britain? Argentina

QUIZ 4: Round 8

1. What is Port Salut – A cheese, a wine, a fish?
    Cheese
2. Did sliced bread first appear in the 1930s,
    1940s or 1950s? 1930s
3. What miracle did Jesus perform at the
    wedding feast of Cana? Water into wine
4. What are 'Ben and Jerry' famous for? Ice-
    cream
5. What name is given to the Swiss dish where
    food is dipped into melted cheese using
    skewers? Fondue
6. What nuts are used to make Marzipan –
    Almonds, walnuts or cashews? Almonds
7. From the milk of which animal is real
    mozzarella made? The Buffalo
8. Button, oyster and shitake are varieties of
    what? Mushroom
9. Traditionally, for how many minutes is steak
    tartare cooked? Zero – it's eaten raw
10. What are habanero and scotch bonnet
    varieties of? Chili pepper

QUIZ 4: Round 9

1. What superhero's real name is Clark Kent? Superman
2. From what fruit is champagne made? Grapes
3. What is the largest country in South America? Brazil
4. What breakfast cereal was said to go 'Snap, Crackle and Pop'? Kellogg's Rice Krispies
5. In New York's JFK airport, what does the 'K' stand for? Kennedy
6. Is there a net in the game of squash? No
7. From what country did the USA buy Alaska? Russia
8. From what country did the USA buy Louisiana? France
9. What sport follows the Queensbury Rules – Boxing, weightlifting or fishing? Boxing
10. With which band was Freddie Mercury the lead singer – Bread, Soap or Queen? Queen

QUIZ 4: Round 10

1. Dot-Matrix, Laser and Inkjet are types of what technological device? Printers
2. What type of software are Chrome, Explorer and Safari? Internet browsers
3. What does the 'V in 'VDU' stand for? VISUAL display unit
4. What country has the internet domain '.ru'? Russia
5. What would you use Hotmail, Gmail or Outlook to check? Emails
6. What company bought Instagram in 2012? Facebook
7. What is the total number of characters that are allowed in a tweet on Twitter? 140
8. What company was founded by, amongst others, Mark Zuckerberg in 2004? Facebook
9. What did the island of Tuvalu do with their '.tv' internet domain in 1998? They leased it/ sold it
10. What are C++, Visual Basic and FORTRAN? Computer coding languages

QUIZ 5: Round 1

1. Which equestrian sport might feature a pirouette or a half-pass? Dressage
2. Which Olympic competition features ten separate sub-competitions including 100 Metres and Long Jump? Decathlon
3. Which Brazilian city won the right to host the 2016 Olympics? Rio de Janeiro
4. What is the name of the Olympics' governing body? IOC/International Olympic Committee
5. What is the highest mountain in Greece? Mount Olympus
6. In what country were the 1896 Olympic Games held? Greece
7. True or False – Ireland's first Olympic medal was in painting? True – Look it up!
8. Why were the 1916 Olympics cancelled? World War I
9. What name is given to those who have competed in the Olympics? Olympians
10. Which type of Olympics was first held in 1924? Winter Olympics

QUIZ 5: Round 2

1. What type of craft exploded in May 1937 to cause the Hindenburg disaster? Airship/ Dirigible
2. What famous ship sank on April 15th 1912? RMS Titanic
3. Why did the RMS Lusitania sink on the 7th of May 1915? It was torpedoed
4. What is the name given to a giant wave caused by an earthquake at sea? Tsunami
5. What is the name given to a war where all the participants are from the same country? Civil War
6. Which civil war featured the Roundheads and the Cavaliers? The English Civil War
7. What did the 'Enola Gay' drop first in World War II? An Atomic Bomb
8. What was the nickname of World War II general Erwin Rommel? The Desert Fox
9. Which U.S. TV series centered on the passengers of Oceanic flight 815? Lost
10. Which war ended with the Treaty of Versailles in 1919? World War I

QUIZ 5: Round 3

1. What triangle is the area in the Atlantic where planes and boats have mysteriously disappeared? Bermuda Triangle
2. What *circus* in London is home to a statue of Eros? Piccadilly
3. What square in Moscow is home to the resting place of Lenin? Red Square
4. What cube was the UK's best-selling Christmas gift in 1980? Rubik's Cube
5. What shape describes the HQ of the US Department of Defense? Pentagon
6. What circle do illusionists belong to? The Magic Circle
7. How many sides does a quadrilateral have? Four
8. What imaginary line is half-way between the North and South Poles? The Equator
9. What shape's name comes from the Greek 'kulindros', meaning roller? Cylinder
10. Over what letters of the alphabet would you find a tittle? 'i' and 'j' - it's the dot!

QUIZ 5: Round 4

1. What type of creatures featured in the Jurassic Park movies? Dinosaurs
2. What type of transport was Amelia Earhart associated with? Planes
3. In the Highland Games, what would I do with a caber? Toss or throw it
4. What is the name of the lead-singer with U2? Bono
5. What were the Amstrad CPC464, the ZX Spectrum and the Commodore 64? Computers
6. Traditionally, what colour is a baseball? White
7. What vegetable give Popeye his strength? Spinach
8. What creature has varieties such as Black Widow and Tarantula? Spider
9. What is the national language of Brazil? Portuguese
10. What do Americans celebrate on the 4th of July? Independence Day

QUIZ 5: Round 5

1. In the Star Wars movies, who did Anakin Skywalker become? Darth Vader
2. In 2000, what country was added to rugby's Five Nations – Italy, Spain or Germany? Italy
3. In what UK city is 'EastEnders' set? London
4. With what sport do we normally associate Chris Evert-Lloyd? Tennis
5. In what country do we find communal farms called *Kibbutz*? Israel
6. What is the profession of Mario of Super Mario Brothers fame? Plumber
7. What type of flag traditionally greets the winner of a motor race? Chequered
8. What English Christian name corresponds to the following names – Ivan, Sean, Juan and Giovanni? John
9. What number is directly below '6' on most numeric keypads? '3'
10. What do solar panels harness to make electricity? Sunlight

QUIZ 5: Round 6

1. Which polar inhabitant is the fastest swimming bird? Penguin
2. What beer does Homer Simpson normally drink? Duff Beer
3. What is the principal item in a Panda's diet? Bamboo
4. Shrove Tuesday is another name for what culinary day? Pancake Tuesday
5. How many stripes are on the U.S. flag? 13
6. What type of sea creature is a Portuguese Man of War? Jellyfish
7. 'Polo' aftershave is made by which popular fashion brand? Ralph Lauren
8. What animal is known as "Man's best friend"? The Dog
9. What number is directly below '7' on most numeric keypads? 4
10. What jubilee was celebrated when Queen Elizabeth the second was 50 years on the throne? Golden Jubilee

QUIZ 5: Round 7

1. From what country do we get the soaps 'Neighbours' and 'Home and Away'? Australia
2. On what river does the Oxford and Cambridge boat race take place? The Thames
3. On what would you find a porthole and a deck? A boat or ship
4. In snooker, in a 147 break, what colour is the last ball to be potted? Black
5. What does the 'F' in UFO stand for? Flying
6. The Statue of Liberty holds a book in one hand and what item in the other? Torch
7. Over what country did the Ming Dynasty rule? China
8. What company makes the iPhone? Apple
9. What highwayman had a horse called Black Bess? Dick Turpin
10. After which painter is Rome's Fiumicino airport named? Leonardo da Vinci

QUIZ 5: Round 8

1. What is another name for a 'sleeping policeman', used to slow down cars on roads? Speed bump
2. In televisions, what does the 'L' in LCD stand for? LIQUID Crystal Display
3. Which Asian country used to be called Cathay? China
4. Which saint is associated with the town of Lourdes, France? St. Bernadette
5. If something is described as pneumatic, is it powered by air, water or sunlight? Air
6. In text-speak, what does LOL stand for? Laugh(ing) out loud
7. What general's 'Last Stand' was at the Battle of Little Bighorn? General Custer
8. What is the name of the now disused prison on an island in San Francisco Bay? Alcatraz
9. In boxing, if you 'throw in the towel', what does that mean? You give up
10. In what part of the house would you most likely find a wok or a bain marie? Kitchen

QUIZ 5: Round 9

1. What type of drink might a *merlot* or a *rioja* be? Wine
2. Which is larger, Mars or Earth? Earth
3. What swordsman was famous for leaving a 'Z' behind him? Zorro
4. In the legends of King Arthur, which 'M' was a wizard? Merlin
5. What 'G' is a British overseas territory that borders Spain? Gibraltar
6. Tug-of-War used to be an Olympic event, True or False? True
7. Who was the other half of Stan Laurel's comedy duo? Oliver Hardy
8. What is *Manchego* – a cheese, a board-game or a car manufacturer? A cheese
9. In what country would you find Mount Rushmore? USA
10. What group of people believed in Valhalla and Asgard? Vikings

QUIZ 5: Round 10

1. What, according to the saying, do birds of a feather do? Flock together
2. In semaphore, what 'f' is used to communicate? Flags
3. In what Herman Melville book does Captain Ahab hunt a whale? Moby Dick
4. In *Harry Potter*, what must be given to a house elf to free it? Clothes
5. What country's capital is Prague? Czech Republic
6. Which Shakespeare play is known as 'the Scottish Play' because it is unlucky for actors to use its real name? Macbeth
7. What 'H' is measured using the Carvill scale? Hurricanes
8. With what island do we associate the Manx cat? The Isle of Man
9. In Greek mythology, who turned all he touched to gold? King Midas
10. What 'R' is a sport invented by William Webb-Ellis? Rugby

Tie-Breakers
Answers

20 Tie-Breakers

1. In Lear's poem, who travelled in a 'beautiful pea-green boat'? The Owl and the Pussycat
2. In the Hunger Games films, who plays Katniss Everdeen? Jennifer Lawrence
3. What type of animals are Fiver, Hazel and Bigwig from *Watership Down*? Rabbits
4. In what country is the Yuan the currency? China
5. In the children's series, what is the name of the *Big Red Dog*? Clifford
6. How many degrees do you turn if you make a full circle? 360
7. The word 'Plumber' comes from the Latin word for which metal? Lead
8. In cricket, how many runs do you need for a double-century? 200
9. On what continent would you find Zaire? Africa
10. What is the smallest of the world's oceans? Arctic Ocean
11. Alphabetically, what day of the week comes first? Friday
12. Which children's character is a bear with two birthdays that comes from Peru? Paddington Bear
13. In what country would you find the Taj Mahal? India

14. What 'M' is the name given to a type of animal that carries its babies in a pouch? Marsupial
15. Complete the saying – "A stitch in time, saves ____"? Nine
16. What was Don Quixote known for tilting at? Windmills
17. What is the capital of Scotland? Edinburgh
18. In *Charlie and the Chocolate Factory*, what is Charlie's surname? Bucket
19. What two countries are connected by The Channel Tunnel? England and France
20. How many members were left in *One Direction* after Zayn left? 4